Fish and Fa

readingbasicsplus

 HARPER & ROW, PUBLISHERS NEW YORK HAGERSTOWN SAN FRANCISCO LONDON
1817

STANDARD BOOK NUMBER 06-517004-0

1976 PRINTING

CONTENTS

CONTRIBUTORS

DOLORES R. AMATO   LYNETTE SAINE GAINES   JOSEPH A. LUCERO
A. DICKSON CARROLL   ERIC P. HAMP   MATTIE CLAYBROOK WILLIAMS
CHERIE A. CLODFELTER   PHILLIP L. HARRIS

Special acknowledgment to Marilyn Buckley Hanf.

Plane

The Plane

plane

"Meg! Ben!" said Tim.
"Look at what I have.
I want to make it go up.
And I can't.
Can you help me, Meg?
Can you, Ben?"

"Tim," said Ben.

"You have to have a  .

A  can make the <u>plane</u> go."

"You want a  ?" said Meg.

"I can make a  ."

5

plane

"Here," said Meg.
"This is what you want."

"It can make the <u>plane</u> go far,"
  said Ben.

plane

"Here, Tim," said Meg.

"The ✈ is on the plane.

It can go up.

It can go far up.

Look at it go."

I Am Me

"Can you be a thing?"
said the kitty to me.
"Not me," said I.
"I can not be.
A TV is a thing.
And a swing is a thing.
A thing is a thing.
And I am me."

swing

8

The Kitty

"I have a name," said Ben.

"Pat, you have a name.

And you have a name, Tim.

Not the kitty.

What can we name it?"

"A kitty is fun," said Tim.

"We can name it Fun."

"Fun is not a name," said Pat.

"Fun is what we have."

"Tim is a name," said Tim.

"We can name the kitty Tim."

"Look," said Pat.

"We can't name it Tim.

 Your name is Tim."

"Ben! Tim!" said Pat.

"I have a name!

It is a name.

And it is not a name."

"What?" said Ben.

"A name that is not a name?

What is it?"

"Happy!" said Pat.

"We can name your kitty Happy.

That is what your kitty is.

Look at it!"

What Can Live Here?

A lion can live here.

A zebra can live here.

A zebra can have fun here.

It can play here.

It can be happy here.

So can a lion.

lion

zebra

16

A fish can live here.

It is happy in the water.

Look at it go.

fish

water

A <u>zebra</u> can't live where a <u>fish</u> can.

zebra

fish

A fish can't live where a zebra can.

18

Can a lion live where a fish can?

lion

You can live where a lion lives.

Is this so?

You can live where a fish lives.

Is this so?

S and S

I live here. Pat lives here.

Ben and Tim find the .
Ben finds the .

I have a name.

Meg and Pat have names.

Do you have the green can?

Do you have the green cans?

| thing | make | come |
| things | makes | comes |

Horse

Ride That Horse!

D d F f M m

A  is in the .
A is in the .
A is in the .
Name the things in the .

26

What Do You Know!

"I know you can't be happy,"
said Mrs. Wills.
"You can look happy.
Can't you?"

"OK, Mom," said Ben.

school

"I can't look happy," said Ben.
"Mrs. Green will not be in school.
And school will not be fun."

"I know," said Meg.
"And I know that it can't be helped.
So come on."

school

street

woman

car

"Can you help me?"

said a <u>woman</u> in a <u>car</u>.

"I can't find the <u>school</u>.

Do you know where it is?"

"We can help you," said Meg.

"We know where it is.

It is not far.

It is up this street."

"That woman looks happy," said Ben.

"What is the woman going to do in school?"

woman

"What do you know!" said Ben.

"It is that happy woman."

"This will be fun!" said Meg.

"Are you happy?

Are you?"

Big Cat Is Here

"Big Cat is here,"
said Little Mouse.
"So I have to go."

"Do not go," said Big Cat.
"I know you.
Your name is Little Mouse.
Come here, Little Mouse.
Look at what I have."

Cat

Mouse

34

"I can't," said Little Mouse.
"I have to go to the
mouse house."

"Is this your house?"
said Big Cat.
"Is this where you live?
Can I come in and play?"

35

Cat

"OK," said Little <u>Mouse</u>.

"This is my house.

This is where I live.

Come on in and play, Big <u>Cat</u>."

"I can't come in," said Big Cat.

"Help me, Little Mouse, help me!

Your house is little.

I am big."

"So you are," said Little Mouse.
"So you are.
I am happy my house
is so little.
And am I happy you are
so big!"

Mouse

Hair

Want hair?

Big hair?

Little hair?

Fun hair?

Play hair?

Make hair?

Find the hair that you like.

What is this thing?

Can it be hair?

Can hair look like this?

Ball

Play Ball!

"What are we going to do?" said Ben.

"Where can we play?

It looks like we can't do a thing."

"I know what," said Meg.

"Here is my ball.

We can play.

And I can be first."

ball

"OK, Meg, you can be first," said Pat.

"Get the ball, Tim."

"It is so far up," said Tim.

"It looks little."

"Here it comes," said Pat.

"Tim, look where you are going.

Do not do that!"

"Help me," said Tim.
"Get help!"

"I will help Tim," said Meg.
"I'll help him.
  I know I can help him."

"First Tim!
Now me!" said Meg.

"What can we do?" said Pat.
"Where can we find help?
I'll go and look."

workers

The <u>workers</u> helped Meg and Tim.

What Can We Make?

I can blow  .

You can blow  .

Meg, Pat, Ben, and Tim can

blow  .

A <u>rabbit</u> can blow  .

 can be fun to make.

What can we make?

rabbit

47

where

live lives

first

Mrs. Green

Dad

do

helped

him

kitty

like likes

you your

Mom

know knows

will

that

a

thing

are

Pudding

Now You Can Make Pudding

It is not hard to make pudding.

 pudding

First, you will have to get

cup

pudding mix

spoon

milk

bowl

banana

dishes

Now you can get to work.

Then you work like this.

This is what you do now.

Then your <u>pudding</u> will look like this.

pudding

pudding

Did Mom and Dad like it?
Did the puppy like it?

puppy